COGNITIVE BIAS COULD GET YOU KILLED!

by

Christopher Prince

Introduction

You are one of the main characters in a detective novella. You are about to find yourself at the center of a mystery where your decisions could be the difference between life and death. Throughout the story, you will be asked numerous questions, some minor and some major. Since this is an interactive story designed to help you identify your own cognitive biases, you will be expected to formulate answers to these questions in your own mind.

As a reminder, whenever you are asked a question by one of the story's other characters, you will see a hashtag (#) which indicates you should pause your reading and consider your answer before proceeding through the story. In some cases, questions will be discussed right away; at other times, they will be discussed later in the story.

While the following story addresses dozens of common cognitive biases, it's important to understand that there is no concrete list of cognitive biases. Rather, psychologists and behavioral economists have identified cognitive biases going back decades and continue to identify them. Some cognitive biases are referred to by different names, and others could be considered a combination of biases. Not all experts agree on every aspect of cognitive bias, yet there is widespread agreement that cognitive bias clouds rationality in human judgment.

By the end of the story, you will not become an expert in cognitive bias or retain all the information you learn about each cognitive bias. Yet you will discover the most commonly identified cognitive biases and come to realize your own level of bias so that you can be better prepared how to be a more critical thinker.

The following story depicts some controversial social issues, and many of the characters make comments that you might disagree with or find objectionable. Don't get frustrated and toss the book aside. The depictions are done for very specific reasons, as you will come to understand through the course of the story. Good luck. And remember to keep your head on a swivel.

Chapter 1

It was a rainy Sunday night in Los Angeles, and I was finishing out the weekend the way I started it, getting ready to stalk some philanderer around town so his wife would have the goods on him when the divorce papers were filed. Sneaking behind parked cars and snapping covert portraits of illicit smooching isn't exactly my idea of letting loose on the weekend, but I guess it beats the usual drab routine of background checks and skip traces.

I'm Jack Wilshire, private detective. I've been running this racket from a downtown office for about ten years, ever since I retired from the LAPD after nearly losing my leg in a shootout with a drug runner, over near the LA River on the Eastside of downtown. Back then it was abandoned warehouses and decaying brick walk-ups that haven't been livable since the Roosevelt Administration. Now it's an arts district with hipsters waxing philosophical at outdoor cafes, sipping pinot noir and nibbling avocado toast like an aloof Parisian.

Little could I have imagined, lying there in a pool of blood clinging desperately to my life, the colossal movement that would transform the deteriorating world around me over the next decade. Spurred by a housing crisis and an easy money banking policy, billions were poured into real estate development all over Los Angeles. State-of-the-art high rises, luxury apartment complexes, and posh hotels supplanted the old parking garages, empty warehouses, and single-room-occupancies that housed the fringe of society.

The spartan downtown skyline metamorphosized into an expansive cityscape more representative of a metropolis of four million people, but triggered a tsunami of demographic and cultural changes that left the city with the worst humanitarian crisis in its history.

Tens of thousands of homeless meander the streets of Los Angeles now, hunting for food by day and erecting tents along Skid Row and under freeway overpasses by night. These huddled masses are the excess waste, the soiled residue, the collateral damage of urban progress. Looking out the window from my humble, one-room, second-story office, I can estimate the number of new downtown developments merely by adding up all the new homeless encampments on the sidewalks below me. That's because many of the new downtown developments replaced old decaying tenements, pushing the most marginal of LA's residents out into the streets.

I've been working out of the same office on the northern end of Little Tokyo since I left the force. I'm right on the edge of El Pueblo de Los Angeles, the site where forty-four settlers of Native American, African and European heritage journeyed more than a thousand miles across the desert to form a village that is now the sprawling suburban metropolis of Los Angeles.

So I've seen a lot of changes over the years. And I knew right away something was different when you came bounding through my office door.

You obviously didn't have the time or inclination to grab an umbrella on the way out the door, because you stand before me now, drenched from the rare LA rain. The short shallow breaths and the look in your eye tell me you're not here to surveil a worker's comp recipient. This is something more serious.

I still have about a half hour before my date with the philanderer, so I offer you a cup of stale coffee and grab a footstool from the closet, so you'll have something to sit on. I'm not used to entertaining guests; most of my client relations are done over a smartphone. I apologize for the mess of paperwork sitting on my desk and spilling out of filing cabinets, and then I ask you to give me the low-down.

After a few slurps of coffee, you gather enough breath to get me up to speed. You just moved to LA a couple of weeks ago. You're an independent filmmaker, and you've come to LA to produce a documentary about the legalization of marijuana. Lately, a lot of states have begun to legalize marijuana because of its purported medical benefits and in the name of criminal justice reform. You want to document whether legalization is working. So you moved into a furnished studio apartment in an old converted hotel on Fifth Street, not far from the LA Mission.

You had barely gotten your feet on the ground in Los Angeles when things got unnerving. A little more than a week after moving in, you were walking back from conducting an interview in Mission Junction on the north end of downtown. As you walked up the concrete steps of your apartment building, you saw a package you had shipped to yourself before setting off for LA. If you had not bent down to grab the package, a bullet would have wedged into your skull. Someone had fired at you from across the street. As you faceplanted into the concrete stoop, you could hear footsteps scurrying away from you.

You reported the incident to police but ultimately dismissed it as a random risk of urban living. That is, until two nights later, when glancing out your third-floor apartment window you were nearly struck again by a bullet which shattered the glass inches from your face, projecting shards into your cheeks and knocking you to the hardwood floor. It didn't take a seasoned detective to tell you this was no random act; someone was targeting you.

Being new to the city, you can't imagine who could possibly have an axe to grind with you. The police are working the case but have no leads. You know they're overwhelmed by mounting incidents of downtown crimes, but you don't have the luxury of waiting patiently for LA's Finest to solve the case. So, you've come to me.

After taking it all in, I stand up and pour a mug of black joe for myself. The night is going to be even longer than I anticipated. I take a sip, lean on the corner of my desk, and give you a final once-over before opening my mouth to speak.

"Listen, I want you to understand how I work," I explain. "This is a dangerous case, and it's easy to let emotions get in the way of the facts. If we're going to solve this case and keep you alive, we need to follow the evidence and be as rational as we can. Our biggest enemy, outside of whoever is trying to kill you, is cognitive bias."

You flash me a curious look and ask me to elaborate. I oblige. "Cognitive biases are systematic patterns of deviation from rationality and are often studied in psychology and behavioral economics. Instead of thinking rationally through every single piece of information presented to us, we tend to use heuristics, or mental shortcuts, to come to simple explanations.

"Now, the first thing you have to understand about cognitive biases is that they are not bad in and of themselves. In fact, cognitive biases are necessary for survival, and they were instilled in us through millions of years of evolution. When you hear a child scream, or smell something burning, or see what looks like the tail of a snake, you don't have time to think rationally through what might be going on. Your brain uses these shortcuts, these cognitive biases, to survive. It would be impossible to communicate or to get much of anything done if we didn't have cognitive biases.

"But there are also many problems with cognitive biases. Neurological shortcuts often cause us to draw the wrong conclusions about events. They trick us into making bad decisions. The lead us into unproductive conflicts.

"And there's an even darker side to cognitive biases. Cognitive biases are exploited by some politicians, fringe websites and enemy governments to make us ignore cold hard facts in favor of unfounded, wild conspiracies. Some powerful people manipulate our innate cognitive biases to gain power, drive us against each other, and make us question the truth of everything, all for their own benefit. The exploitation of cognitive bias even led to the murder of six million people merely because of their religion."

After taking all that in for a moment, you ask me what all this has to do with your case. It's not the first time I've been asked that question.

"Listen, if you decide to hire me, we're going to work side by side in solving this case. Whenever we question somebody or uncover a key piece of evidence, I'm going to turn to you and ask your input. You will find yourself in many situations, some mundane and some dire, where you will have to make a rational judgment. In each instance, I will ask you for your input and give you time to consider an answer. And if you should succumb to a cognitive bias, I will tell you and explain to you the nature of that particular bias. So hopefully, over the course of this investigation, you will learn to identify your own cognitive biases and be better equipped to avoid them in order to make more rational judgments. But never forget the stakes. Cognitive bias could get you killed."

As you take in the gravity of the situation, I ask you to consider your own susceptibility to cognitive bias. Naturally, we haven't discussed any specific cognitive biases yet. But you know what bias is generally. "Do you think you're a biased person? How biased do you think you are on scale of 1-10, with 1 being not biased at all and 10 being extremely biased?

#

"Now think about other people. How biased do you think the average person is on a scale of 1-10? Are they more or less biased than you, or about the same?

#

"And finally, how confident are you in your ability to decipher clues and solve this case on a scale of 1-10, with 1 being no confidence and 10 being extremely confident?"

#

Up to this point, we haven't discussed payment. Clients are always eager for me to help solve their problems, but not so eager to turn over the cabbage to pay for it. So that's something we need to get out of the way before proceeding.

"I typically offer my clients a couple of options. One, you can pay a flat fee of $3500 and I'll stay on the case until it's solved or we reach a dead end. Or two, you can pay me $150 per hour for as long as I'm on the case. Which would you prefer?

#

"Well, this just happens to be your first test of cognitive bias. It's called The Ambiguity Effect. The ambiguity effect is a cognitive bias where decision making is affected by a lack of information, or ambiguity. The effect implies that people tend to select options for which the probability of a favorable outcome is known, over an option for which the probability of a favorable outcome is unknown.

"In this case, many people would opt to pay the flat fee because, although it's a much higher amount, it's tangible and known. It may end up working out that choosing the hourly rate could save you a lot of money, but the outcome – or the total amount paid – cannot be guaranteed. So for that reason, many people would choose to pay the known flat fee."

With the issue of money settled, I look up at the clock. Time is running short before I have to head out on my night's assignment, so I want to make sure I have as much information as possible before we start the case. I ask you if you've had any significant contact with anyone since you arrived in Los Angeles.

You tell me you didn't know anyone in Los Angeles prior to arriving. And since you got here, you've had limited contact with anyone. You met the apartment manager who lives in your building and he showed you your apartment. He seemed like a nice enough guy.

Then you mention you've conducted one interview so far for your documentary. It was with the owner of a downtown marijuana dispensary. He was very affable and answered all your questions about running a legal pot shop.

You hesitate for a moment, and a look of revelation comes over your face. I give you a moment to collect your thoughts, and you recall something odd that happened at the end of the interview. You have trouble recalling the exact exchange, but fortunately you uploaded video of the interview to your cloud storage. So you quickly load the video onto your smartphone and cue the video to near the end.

On the screen is the pot shop owner, late thirties, with a goatee and casually dressed. As the video starts to play, you mention to the pot shop owner that you've been having trouble sleeping lately and heard that hemp products are good sleep aids. The pot shop owner concurs, reaching into his desk and pulling out a couple of wrapped edibles. He holds them up for you to see.

"I'm happy to give you a free sample if you want. We have a couple of good edibles to choose from. The one on the left has an 87% rate of effectiveness in helping people fall asleep and sleep straight through the night. The one on the right is effective for most people, but in 13% of cases, it doesn't work and causes severe heart palpitations and nightmares. Which one would you be interested in trying?"

You take a moment and give that some thought.

#

At this point, I pause the video and ask you what choice you made. I explain that what the pot shop owner presented you was something called The Framing Effect, which is a common cognitive bias.

"The framing effect is a cognitive bias where people make choices based on whether the options are presented with positive or negative connotations. In this case, the pot shop owner framed the first edible in a positive light, saying that it was 87% effective. Then he framed the second edible in a negative light, explaining that the rate of inefficacy and bad side effects is 13%. From the information presented, both edibles have the exact same rate of efficacy: 87%. The only thing we don't know is if the first edible has the negative side effects of the second edible, so that is something you would want to ask.

"But if you chose the first edible instead of the second despite no known differences between the two, you probably succumbed to the framing effect. This is a common ploy used by marketers and salespeople who try to push you into making one purchase option over another."

At this point, I restart the video, which is right near the end of the interview. You ask the pot shop owner to elaborate on the process of obtaining a state license to sell marijuana products. He gives you a curious look. "Uh, why do you wanna know about that?"

You tell him you want to better understand the regulatory side of the industry. He snaps back, "Well, then you can ask the State of California about that. I've given them enough of my time and money. Listen, I gotta get back to work. Best of luck on your documentary."

The pot shop owner stands up abruptly as the video goes dead.

"Well, that was a little awkward," I admit. "He's someone we'll want to follow up on." In the meantime, I ask if you've had any other encounters.

You think for a moment and then recall a strange incident that happened shortly before the shootings. You were walking down your block late one night and noticed a homeless guy standing outside the bar near the corner of your street. He was banging on a window and shouting angrily, although no one else was there. You shouted at him from across the street to stop all his carrying on. He suddenly turned around and flashed you an angry glare. He shouted, "You have the nerve to get on my case when I went out of my way to help you!" You had never met this homeless guy before, and you weren't about to challenge a raving wanderer in the middle of the night. So you just walked away and headed home.

"Okay," I chime in. "This is a decent lead. Since you hadn't met him before that night, I want you to give me some adjectives to describe what kind of person you think the homeless guy is. Just think of two or three adjectives you would use to describe who he is as a person."

#

Looking back up at the clock, I realize my time is just about expired. I tell you I only have a couple of minutes remaining. Before you go, I ask if you can think of anyone else you may have interacted with or had any kind of conflict with.

You tell me you can recall only one other person: Your upstairs neighbor. On three consecutive nights before the shootings, you heard loud music coming from the upstairs apartment late at night. The first two nights, you went upstairs and politely asked the neighbor to turn down the music, which he did. But you lost your patience on the third night and telephoned your apartment manager to complain. You don't know what was done about it, but you did notice the loud music stopped shortly thereafter and didn't happen again on subsequent nights.

I interject, "Okay, this is another good lead. I realize you don't know who the upstairs neighbor is, but based upon the little you've encountered with him, what occupation do you think the upstairs neighbor has?"

#

"Now that you've considered what occupation your upstairs neighbor has, what do you think is more probable: that your upstairs neighbor is an elementary schoolteacher, or an elementary schoolteacher who has a drinking problem?"

#

My time for the night is up, and I tell you I need to head out and start the surveillance on my other case. You and I agree to meet at your apartment tomorrow morning. I leave you with a word of caution. "For tonight, keep your head on a swivel. And take notes on anyone or anything you see." With that, we shake hands and head our separate ways.

Chapter 2

I arrive at your apartment a little groggy. Last night went a little later than expected. I tell you that my philandering friend hit three different bars down on Broadway visiting his pals. He finally made the rendezvous with his mistress at a chic wine bar near the Toy District well after midnight. It was worth the wait. I got the money shot as they were toasting cabernet, leaning in to share a tender candlelit kiss.

I apologize for my appearance, as I didn't have time to shave. I recommend we start the investigation with the apartment manager. I noticed on the way in that he has a first-floor apartment with a clear view of the street where the shots were fired. I want to verify whether he saw anything.

So you and I head to the first floor and rap on the apartment manager's door. After a few moments, we hear a click of a lock, and the door swings open to reveal a man of about thirty dressed in shorts and sneakers. He does a double-take upon seeing you, then chuckles.

"Sorry, I thought you were Riley for a second."

He explains that Riley is the former tenant who used to live in your apartment. He tells us he's about the head out for a morning jog, but I explain why we're there and get him to agree to give us a few minutes of his time. I ask if he remembers seeing anything the night of either shooting.

"I was in my bedroom in the back when I heard both shootings. By the time I got to the front window, I didn't see anything. Honestly, my first thought is that it could be some crazy homeless guy. The homeless problem is out of control down here, and something like 80% of homeless people are mentally ill. It's really sad, but living on the streets is very stressful and causes homeless people to become mentally ill. I wouldn't be surprised if it was one of them."

I press the apartment manager to try and recall anything unusual he may have seen. After a moment, he suddenly recalls something. "You know, I did notice one of those delivery vans parked across the street on the night of both shootings. It was for one of those marijuana dispensaries. You know, those folks do deliveries now."

This revelation immediately piques our interest. The pot shop owner you interviewed got a little strange when you asked about obtaining a state license. We wonder if the delivery van was his. We thank the apartment manager and finally let him free to take his jog. I tell you I'm going to run a background check on the pot shop and see if I can dig anything up. You turn to go wait in your apartment while I head out the front door to return to my office.

Just as you see the front door swing open, however, you notice a homeless guy standing across the street with his back to a wall. You tell me it's the same guy you saw raving the night before the first shooting. I suggest you keep your distance, and I head across the street and cautiously approach the homeless man.

He has the weathered look of a man in his fifties, although years of living on the streets probably make him look about twenty years older than he is. I tell him I'm investigating the shootings and ask him if he knows anything about them. He shrugs and says there are shootings every day in the city.

Then I press him about the night you saw him screaming and banging the window. He thinks for a moment and then recalls.

"Oh, right. Yeah, I kind of lost my head that night. I got down to the soup kitchen late and missed dinner. And then someone stole my sleeping bag. I just totally lost it."

Then I ask him why he shouted at you and claimed that he was helping you. The homeless man grimaces and mutters, "He knows why." At that point, he protests continuing the conversation and marches off down the sidewalk.

I cross the street to inform you of my conversation. We are both curious as to some of the homeless man's comments. But I want to focus on the reasons he gave for being so upset that night.

"When you first told me about your encounter with the homeless man, I asked you to give me some adjectives to describe what kind of person you think the homeless guy is. Do you remember what came to mind? Did you think he might have been a crazy person or a volatile person? Or did it occur to you that maybe he was just having a bad night? Many people would have assumed his behavior that night was indicative of his overall personality, when in reality he was merely responding with anguish over his setbacks of the day.

"If you judged his behavior as being typical of his personality, then you succumbed to a cognitive bias known as the fundamental attribution error. The fundamental attribution error is the tendency for people to over-emphasize dispositional, or personality-based explanations for behaviors observed in others, while under-emphasizing situational explanations. In other words, people have a cognitive bias to assume that a person's actions depend on what kind of person they are rather than on the social and environmental forces that influence them.

"Ask yourself, how would you feel if you had just been deprived of dinner and a comfortable place to sleep? Do you think maybe you could lose your cool? In order to make more accurate assessments of someone's personality or character, you would want to observe them over a longer period in many contexts."

We agree to meet back at your apartment later after I run a background check on the pot shop. So I head back to the office and do some research. It turns out your friend the pot shop owner has a bit of a checkered history. He was arrested a few times for illegal marijuana sales, although this was before legalization. I also discover his name is associated with about a dozen businesses scattered around Los Angeles, all having something to do with hemp or marijuana. That in itself is not suspicious. But the hair on my neck stood up when I found out that not a single one of his businesses had applied for or received a license to operate a cannabis shop. So, now we know why he ended your interview so abruptly.

Armed with this new evidence, we decide to pay the pot shop owner another visit. We enter his storefront right near the bustling Santee Alley in the Fashion District. Most of the shops in this part of town sell name-brand knock-offs for pennies on the dollar. Getting buzzed through a security door, we see that the pot shop has an assorted collection of cannabis products, from edibles, to oils, to good old-fashioned pot. A maître d' of sorts, a rather brawny fellow with a long ponytail, leads us back to a small office in the back, where the pot shop owner is seated behind a desk. Needless to say, he isn't real pleased with seeing your face again.

I tell him about the shootings and ask him if he knows anything about a cannabis delivery van that was parked on the block. He blows it off and mutters something about there being a ton of cannabis shops delivering downtown. I'm getting a little agitated by his reticence, so I bring up the license issue. Specifically, the fact that he doesn't have one. Well, if I was looking to light a fire, I struck the right match. He launches from his chair, screams something about minding our own business, and marches us out the front door. No free samples this time around.

So we return to your apartment to interview the last of the people you interacted with, the upstairs neighbor. As luck would have it, he's walking up the stairs to the building just as we arrive. We stop him and ask him if he has a minute to talk. He looks tired and irritated, explaining he just got off work and wants to go rest. I find that a bit curious given that it's so early in the day.

"Listen, I know it's none of our business, but you were recently up late several nights in a row playing music. I wouldn't take you for a guy who works the early shift."

The neighbor nods, "Yeah, that was my vacation week. I'm usually in bed early and up early. I have to jump on a bus before dawn to get to my job across town." I ask him what he does for a living. He hesitates before answering. "I manage a gun shop."

We let that sink in, and then I tell him the reason for stopping him. You ask if he remembers anything unusual the night of the shootings.

"Look, I already told the cops everything I know, which is nothing. I heard the shots but didn't see anything. And quite honestly, I'm not going to lift a finger to help you. You have some nerve calling the apartment manager on me. Stay outta my business!"

With that, the neighbor pushes through the front door and stomps down the hallway and out of view. I turn to you.

"Okay, let's revisit a couple of issues. When you first told me about the encounters with your neighbor, I asked you what you thought he probably did for a living. Do you remember your answer? Well, did you think he probably worked some kind of second-shift or night job since he was up so late? As it turns out, he works the early shift. If you assumed he worked a later-shift job, you may have succumbed to a clustering illusion.

"A clustering illusion a cognitive bias where we erroneously assume that a streak or cluster of events is representative of the whole, when in reality you can't make valid judgments based on small samples from random distributions. The illusion is caused by a human tendency to underpredict the amount of variability likely to appear in a small sample of random or semi-random data. In this situation, you had just moved into the apartment and had no idea about the regular behavioral patterns of the upstairs neighbor.

"You may have formed an opinion about his profession, or whether he even had a job at all, based on a small sample of three nights of activity. As it turns out, those three nights represented a temporary deviation from his normal routine. To combat against the clustering illusion, always ask yourself whether you have sufficient data to determine a long-observed pattern, or whether the data is too small a sample size to make a sound judgment. The law of large numbers would have allowed you to monitor his routine over a much longer time, and you would have realized he is rarely up late because he works the early shift.

"And remember when I asked you which is more likely, that your neighbor is an elementary schoolteacher, or an elementary schoolteacher with a drinking problem? If you thought it was more likely he was an elementary schoolteacher with a drinking problem, you fell victim to a conjunction fallacy. A conjunction fallacy is a cognitive bias in which we believe that two events happening in conjunction is more probable than one of those events happening alone. It is statistically impossible for your neighbor to more likely be an alcoholic schoolteacher than just a teacher. Of the entire population of elementary schoolteachers, only a small percentage are also alcoholics.

"So, how can people make such an obvious error in calculating probability? This is a hotly debated topic. But generally speaking, we so strongly want to make meaning out of the events around us that we ignore simple rules of math. Since we don't know many elementary schoolteachers who stay up late blasting music, we cling to the idea of alcoholism because it helps to make sense of their aberrant behavior. We have a much stronger emotional connection to that explanation, so we ignore basic math."

At this point, we head up to your third-floor apartment to evaluate what we've discovered so far. Your apartment contains a handful of inexpensive pieces that came furnished with the apartment, including a sofa, reading chair, coffee table and television stand. We take a seat and go over the available evidence. So far, we've identified three persons of interest, people we might call suspects. I lean forward and give you a serious look. "Which suspect are you most curious of right now? Which suspect do you have the strongest emotional reaction to at this moment?"

#

"Some people will choose the upstairs neighbor because of availability bias. Availability bias is a mental shortcut that relies on immediate examples that come to mind. People tend to heavily weigh their judgments toward more recent information, making new opinions biased toward the latest news. Since the neighbor was the last person interviewed, he is fresher in mind or more susceptible to availability bias.

"Availability bias may be stronger in less critical matters though, such as when sports fans evaluate which teams were the greatest in history. Sports fans typically believe more recent teams were better than teams in the past because details about newer teams can be recalled much more easily. But in this situation, we're trying to solve the mystery of who's trying to kill you, and the events are much more recent. So you may have been able to overcome availability bias to evaluate each suspect on the merits of the evidence against them."

Now that we've discussed the suspects, I turn our attention to next steps. "I want you to consider anything that you would most like to investigate at this point. Think about what questions you would ask at this point in the investigation and what things you would like to investigate more. I'm going to give you a little longer to think about this one."

#

I can see you're mulling over the possibilities, so I give you some time. After I see you've settled on some ideas, I inquire.

"So let me ask you, did you think mostly about the three main suspects? Did you consider investigating anything not related to the three suspects? Did you consider trying to ask questions that prove someone's guilt, or did you think about finding evidence that would rule out someone's guilt?

"If you mostly thought about investigating the three suspects or finding evidence to prove their guilt, you may have been influenced by confirmation bias. Confirmation bias is the tendency to search for, interpret, favor, and recall information in a way that confirms or strengthens one's prior personal beliefs or hypotheses. In other words, we quickly jump to a hypothesis and then seek evidence to confirm our hypothesis. The danger of confirmation bias is that we ignore counterevidence or completely fail to look for counterevidence that would reshape our hypothesis and perhaps lead us to the truth.

"Many well-intentioned journalists have come to faulty conclusions because of confirmation bias. Even worse, scores of innocent people have been wrongly convicted of crimes because of overzealous police and prosecutors who were seized with confirmation bias throughout their investigations. Overcoming confirmation bias is not easy, because people are passionate about their beliefs. To avoid confirmation bias, you must be willing to continually challenge your own beliefs and look for counterevidence to contrast against your evidence."

With hours of investigating under our belts, we take a break. You offer me a drink and flip on the television. Much to our shock, staring back at us on the TV screen is the pot shop owner, being led to a police squad car in handcuffs. A news reporter delivers the news, as it seems several downtown cannabis shops were raided by police for operating without a valid state license.

We flash each other a stunned look. So much for taking a break.

Chapter 3

By the time we get back to the Fashion District, the news media and most of the cop cars have pulled out. All that is left are a couple of detectives and a patrolman out front of the pot shop. Luckily, I still have a few pals on the force, so we are allowed in to speak with the lead detective.

It appears that the State of California caught on to the pot shop owner before we did. He's been operating cannabis joints around the city without a license for a couple of years now. It's not uncommon, as a lot of cannabis sellers want to avoid the licensing fees and high taxation that was agreed upon when the state finally relented to legalizing marijuana. The cops didn't just take down the owner. They had every employee sitting in handcuffs on the sidewalk out front before hauling the whole lot of them off to county lockup. I guess it pays to be careful about whom you're working for.

I tell the lead detective about our predicament, and how a pot shop delivery van was seen on your block around the time of both shootings. He motions for us to follow him, and he leads us back to the owner's office in the back of the store. He sits down at the desk and begins to plug away at the computer keyboard. After a minute of studying the computer screen, he nods with satisfaction.

"Well, I'm not supposed to be sharing this information with anyone outside the department. But considering Jack here took a bullet for us years ago, I don't mind helping out a friend. I'm looking back at the delivery schedule on the dates of the shootings, and sure enough, this very cannabis shop made a delivery to your block on both nights."

I look over at you, and I can see that revelation hit you like a cannonball. I give it a moment to sink in before leaning over into your ear.

"Is there anything else you'd like to ask the detective about the delivery schedule while he has it on the screen?"

#

I thank the detective for his time and for bending the rules for us. We hit the pavement again and head back up to your apartment. Walking up the Main Street sidewalk and just as we turn the corner onto Fifth, we both stop in our tracks at what we see at the end of the next block. Parked at a meter right across from your apartment is a pot shop delivery van.

I immediately grab your arm and guide you cautiously down the sidewalk, swinging our heads in all directions frantically trying to detect a sniper. We stay close to the row of buildings across the street as we creep our way adjacent to the delivery van. Arriving directly across from the van, we freeze when we a delivery man sitting in the driver's seat checking his phone.

After a moment, the delivery man slowly exits the driver's door. We brace ourselves for the worst. He closes the door but doesn't appear to have a gun in hand. Suddenly, he spots us staring intently at him, and a look of horror overcomes him. He sprints around the van and the up the sidewalk in a desperate attempt to elude us. We begin the chase.

We stalk him a couple of blocks, but he disappears in a row of bodegas along Winston Street. One of the shop owners standing out front confirms he saw the delivery man run right past him seconds earlier. He asks why we're chasing him, and I tell him we want to question him about the shootings on Fifth Street. The shop owner lights up.

"Oh, yeah! I've seen that same guy on Fifth Street a dozen times. Do you think he's the shooter?"

#

We are just about to answer when suddenly the delivery driver peeks his head out of a bodega, spots us, and takes off again. But this time, he doesn't lose us. We manage to catch up to him in front of an empty space that used to be a sunglass shop and tackle him to the ground. He begs us for mercy.

"Look, I had nothing to do with it! I just got this job a month ago, and I had no idea the owner didn't have a license!"

You and I look at each other dumfounded. We're worried this guy is a hitman, and he's going on about a pot license? I put the heat on him for a minute, demanding he stop playing dumb about the shootings.

"What are you talking about, shootings? Aren't you guys here to arrest me as part of the cannabis shop bust?"

It turns out the delivery driver thinks we're LAPD and we're here to arrest him like they arrested all the other employees. He says he was out on delivery when he heard about the bust, and he was just on Fifth Street making the last of his deliveries when he spotted us glaring at him from across the street.

Naturally, we find his explanation suspect. I mean, why would he be so conscientious about finishing deliveries for a company that's probably going to be out of business? He claims he understands our skepticism and asks us to follow him back to the delivery van for proof. We reluctantly agree to escort him back.

Arriving back at the van, I tell him he's not going back into that van by himself. So he instructs you to open the passenger door and grab a bag off the seat, so you do. He then leads us into the apartment building across from your apartment and takes us to a door off the first-floor hallway. After a couple of knocks, a woman opens the door, surprised to see the three of us standing there. She's pale with dark circles under her eyes and a bandanna wrapped around her head.

The delivery driver motions for you to give her the bag. She takes it and a look of relief comes over her face.

"I'm so glad you were able to make it. I heard about the busts that happened today and I was afraid I wouldn't get this. The treatments have been really rough this week and I desperately need something for the nausea. I don't understand why your boss didn't just get the license. You deliver to a lot of people in this building who really need this stuff."

She thanks us again and closes the door, and we look sheepishly at the delivery driver. He confirms that he makes a lot of regular deliveries to people on this block. He explains that the only reason he carried out the last of his deliveries, even after the bust, was because many of his customers are cancer patients. We apologize for the misunderstanding and go our separate ways.

Crossing the street to your apartment, I give you a light pat on the back. "You've learned the hard way about correlation fallacy. Correlation fallacy, sometimes referred to as 'correlation does not imply causation,' is an example of a questionable-cause logical fallacy, in which two events occurring together are erroneously taken to have established a cause-and-effect relationship.

"In this case, you knew the delivery van being present on your block correlated with the shootings. That was alleged by your apartment manager and confirmed by the delivery schedule on the pot shop computer. The question is, was the correlation also cause-and-effect? In other words, did the delivery van driver cause the shootings in addition to being correlated with the shootings?

"Well, did you happen to notice you had a couple of opportunities to challenge the cause-and-effect? Think back to when I asked you whether you had any other questions for the police detective about the delivery schedule. Did it occur to you to ask him whether the pot shop made any other deliveries to your block other than the nights of the shootings? If you had learned that the pot shop made lots of regular deliveries to your block, then that probably would have called into question the relevance of seeing the delivery van the night of the shootings.

"Correlation fallacy is a common cognitive bias, and it riddles a great deal of health science, for example.

Researchers often find correlations between eating certain foods and higher incidents of some diseases and come to the erroneous conclusion that there's a cause-and-effect relationship. In some cases, it's led to decades of bad nutrition advice before the correlation fallacy is exposed.

"To avoid correlation fallacy, you always want to ask a few questions about the two things that correlate. For example, let's take the correlation between vaccines and autism. If you wanted to test cause-and-effect, you would ask how many children took the vaccine and got autism, how many children took the vaccine and didn't get autism, how many children didn't take the vaccine but got autism, and how many children didn't take the vaccine and didn't get autism? If the rate of autism is about the same between the children who did take the vaccine and the children who didn't take the vaccine, then you'd know there is no cause-and-effect.

"It's not really practical to ask all these questions in a case of a couple of shootings and a delivery van, but at the very least you should have found out how frequently that van delivers to your block.

"And by the way, even if you didn't think to ask the police detective about the other deliveries, you received a clue that should have tipped you off. Remember the bodega owner we encountered while chasing the delivery driver? He confirmed he had seen the delivery driver a dozen times on your block. Did that set off any bells for you when you heard him say that?

"If not, then you fell victim to another cognitive bias known as the Semmelweis reflex. The Semmelweis reflex is the tendency to reject new evidence or new knowledge because it contradicts established norms, beliefs, or paradigms. The bodega owner gave you significant new evidence that would challenge the belief of the delivery van being out of the ordinary. But if you were so caught up in the hypothesis of the delivery driver's guilt, you may have ignored this new counterevidence. The Semmelweis reflex is a big reason people succumb to confirmation bias."

I walk you back to your apartment door. At this point, it's been a long day, and you've already spent a good chunk of change with me on the case. We've hit a big dead end, and you're going to have to make a tough decision.

Chapter 4

As I walk you back to your apartment door, we reflect on the fact that we've made some strides in the investigation but still don't have any solid leads. We have three people of interest but nothing tangible implicating anyone. At this point, you've spent the equivalent of a week's salary paying my fee. I always want to make sure that my clients are happy, so I ask you how you would like to proceed.

"Look, I realize you've spent a chunk of money on me so far. If you're happy with our progress, you can continue to pay me to stay on the case. I would also be happy to recommend another private detective if you would prefer to make a change. And of course, you could just forego a private detective altogether and just let the police solve the case. Take a moment and think about the money you've already spent and consider which option you'd be most comfortable choosing."

#

"With this dilemma, there are rational judgments no matter which choice you make. But one choice is driven by a cognitive bias. If you chose to retain my services mainly because of the money you've already spent on me, you would have been influenced by a sunk cost fallacy. A sunk cost fallacy is a cognitive bias where you choose to increase your investment of money or effort based on the sunk cost, or cumulative prior investment, despite new evidence suggesting that the future cost of continuing the behavior outweighs the expected benefit. In other words, you keep throwing money or effort at something merely because you don't want to waste the prior investment.

"This is the same cognitive bias that causes people to continue paying for repairs on an old car rather than just biting the bullet and buying a new car. Sunk cost fallacy is also what causes governments to continue spending millions of dollars on failing projects for fear of wasting previously spent taxpayer dollars.

"But as the old saying goes, if you find yourself in a hole, stop digging. Your decision to continue an activity should be based solely on the cost-benefit analysis of expected future performance. If you feel you haven't gotten sufficient results from my services for what you paid, then you should cut bait and move on."

You tell me you're fine with the results so far and want to continue working together. Just as you insert your key into your apartment door, we suddenly hear someone calling out from down the hallway.

"Hey, Riley!" We turn around and see a woman walking towards us. As she gets within a few feet, her smile turns to surprise. "Oh, sorry. I thought you were Riley, the previous tenant in your apartment. You look alike from a distance."

You tell her no problem, that it's not the first time someone told you that. You explain that Riley doesn't live there anymore. She's a bit surprised, although she says she didn't know Riley very well. "I've seen Riley talking to the homeless people in the neighborhood, and I just got shouted at by some homeless guy and I wanted to see if Riley knew him. You know, I'm getting pretty sick of the homeless problem down here. I think LA should do what they did last year down in Westport. They outlawed homeless encampments and started arresting people who sleep in public places. They say it will motivate people to get jobs and get off the streets. I think it's a good idea. What do you think about them passing a law like that around here?"

You give that a thought for a second and rate the idea on a scale from 1-10.

#

The woman apologizes for the mix-up and heads down the hallway towards her apartment. A light bulb goes off in my head, and I turn to you.

"Did you happen to pick up on the clue you just got from your neighbor? She's the second person who initially mistook you for Riley, the previous tenant in your apartment. Your apartment manager said the same thing earlier. Now I'm starting to wonder whether we've been on the wrong trail all along. Up to now, we've been investigating people who might have had a motive to kill you. But what if no one had a motive to kill you? What if someone had a motive to kill Riley and mistook the two of you?"

We both reflect on that for a moment, realizing the can of worms this might open up. It would mean that everything we did so far was a dead end, and we'd have to restart the investigation. This is not exactly a sure-fire lead, but it might be worth exploring. I ask you for your thoughts.

"Listen, it's your money. We can continue investigating the suspects we already have, or we can spend some time and energy now investigating whether this was a case of mistaken identity. Which would you prefer?"

#

"You might have noticed this was another decision that could be affected by sunk cost fallacy. If you made your decision based solely on what you thought was the most fruitful course of action, then you avoided sunk cost fallacy. But if you were motivated at all to continue investigating the same suspects merely because of the time you've already invested in that course of inquiry, then you committed a sunk cost fallacy."

We both agree that the current list of suspects needs further exploration. However, we think it's wise to do a little digging to see if anyone might have been out to get Riley.

The only problem is, we somehow need to figure out who and where Riley is.

Chapter 5

As we head down the old, creaky elevator to the first floor to pay a visit to the apartment manager, I acknowledge that we're about to make a major shift in the investigation. We're not done with the other suspects yet, but since we're giving them a temporary reprieve, I'm interested in knowing your thoughts about them.

"Think about the pot shop owner, the homeless man, and the upstairs neighbor. What makes you suspicious of each of them?"

#

"In criminal investigations, police and prosecutors are trained to focus on which suspects have the means, motive and opportunity for committing a crime. That's considered the most rational way to investigate and prosecute crimes. When you considered your suspicions of the three suspects, did you focus on how each might have had the means, motive and opportunity to shoot at you?

"Or were your suspicions based upon a generalized belief about their lifestyle or role? In other words, did the fact that one was a marijuana distributor, one was a gun dealer, and one was a homeless man factor into your suspicions? All three of these roles come with a stigma and lead to generalized beliefs, or stereotypes, about who they are as people. Did these stereotypes inflame your suspicions?

"Stereotypes are one example of attribute substitution. Attribute substitution is a cognitive bias in which you must make a judgment that is computationally complex, and instead you substitute a more easily calculated shortcut attribute. For example, when trying to make a judgment about the complex issue of racial inequality, it is much easier to substitute a simple stereotype about one race being inferior to another. It helps you avoid doing the intellectual work of uncovering the more complicated truth.

"This is not to say that the roles of the three suspects are irrelevant to our investigation. The pot shop owner's licensing issue, the upstairs neighbor's access to guns, and the homeless man's desperate circumstances all speak to either means or motive. But harboring suspicions based on their societal roles irrespective of means, motive and opportunity is indicative of attribute substitution."

As we exit the elevator, we head down the hallway and stop at the apartment manager's door. After a few knocks, the apartment manager emerges. He looks rather exasperated and explains the rough day he's had.

"It's been one of those days. I've gotten like 100 calls from tenants. Seems like everything is going at once: toilets, sinks, you name it."

We explain to him that we now have suspicions that Riley, the previous tenant in your apartment, might have been the target of the shootings. Our hypothesis seems to immediately resonate with the apartment manager.

"You know, that makes a lot of sense. You do look a lot like Riley from a distance. And to be honest, I wouldn't be surprised if Riley had gotten involved with some shady people. I probably shouldn't be saying this, but I've witnessed Riley creeping around the neighborhood, looking into people's apartments, and associating with strange characters on the streets. I mean, they're everywhere. I must have gone out 100 times today to get homeless people away from the front door."

We give each other a nod, realizing that we may be on to something. We ask the apartment manager to elaborate, but he doesn't really know much else about Riley. Riley never gave any forwarding address upon moving out, and the apartment manager never met any of Riley's associates. But upon further prodding, the apartment manager suddenly remembers that apartment applications always contain an emergency contact. Yet when we ask to see Riley's application, the apartment manager sours.

"Sorry, that's against company policy. I can't let you see it." He sees the dejected look on our faces and starts to relent. "Look, I could get into a lot of trouble if I give you that information. But I understand you're in a tough bind. Maybe if you guys would help me out, I could let you see Riley's emergency contact. But you gotta give me something decent to make it worth the risk."

I turn to gauge your interest. "This could be a big lead. How much money are you willing to give your apartment manager to give you Riley's emergency contact?"

#

I want to help you get the information, but I don't want you to overpay. So I ask you quietly how much you're willing to pay. "I'm just curious, did you happen to consider an amount around $100? If so, you might have been influenced by anchoring bias. Anchoring is a cognitive bias where you depend too heavily on an initial piece of information offered when making decisions. In this case, the number '100' was mentioned twice by your apartment manager earlier in the conversation. The number '100' acts as an anchor and can impact which number you conceive when asked about payment.

"In this case, the previous mentions of the number are not related to the request of payment. But in many sales contexts, they are. For example, car salesmen typically use a highballing technique to get you to pay more for a car. They propose a price that is much higher than they know you'll pay. But by starting the negotiation excessively high, they anchor you to that number. So then, when they inevitably come down in price, you will feel like you're getting a good deal, even though you may be paying a lot higher than you initially wanted.

"Anchoring bias can involve more than just numbers. You can be anchored to a feeling, a mood, an experience, among many others. For example, if you want to convince your spouse to schedule an expensive vacation, you might first remind them of a past vacation they loved. By anchoring them to that past positive experience, you're more likely to get them to spend the dough on a new vacation."

You and the apartment manager come to an agreement about price, and you hand him the cash. He opens a filing cabinet in the living room and rifles through dozens of applications before finally spotting Riley's. He finds the emergency contact information and writes down a woman's name and telephone number and hands it to you. We thank him for his help and exit the apartment.

Standing in the hallway, you eagerly pull out your smartphone and call the number. Unfortunately, no one answers. Luckily, however, the woman's voicemail reveals she works for a downtown company. Instead of leaving a message, you quickly look up the location of the company. It's getting late in the afternoon, so we decide we'll wait until tomorrow to pay her a visit at her office. For now, it's time to gather a little more intel on Riley before calling it a night.

Chapter 6

I do a quick background check from my smartphone, but I can't find any new addresses or employers for Riley. So we set out to find anyone who might know where Riley is. From what we've been told so far by two people at the apartment, Riley seems to have made a lot of acquaintances in the neighborhood. We meander down the sidewalk looking for anyone who appears to live or work local to the neighborhood. We don't really have much to reference Riley, other than the fact that you apparently look similar. Not surprisingly, the first few people we encounter have no idea who we're talking about.

As we pass near the Los Angeles Mission, a woman out front calls to us. She stands in front of a donation box and asks for a small donation to help feed the homeless. I turn to you and ask, "How inclined are you to give a small donation to the Mission on a scale of 1-10?"

#

As we continue down the sidewalk, we stop in front of a coffee house around the corner from your apartment. Assuming Riley was a coffee drinker like everyone else in Los Angeles, we head inside and question the barista. Our instinct was right.

"Oh, yeah, I know who you're talking about," the barista recalls. "Riley would come in a few times a week. I got a little creeped out though, because several times when I was leaving work, I would see Riley circling an apartment building and looking into the windows. Almost like Riley was stalking someone."

The barista doesn't know anything else about Riley, so we offer a thank you and go on our way. A couple of doors down we pass a newsstand and give the same spiel to the newsstand vendor. He also recalls who Riley is. "Yeah, your friend Riley is a strange bird. Always walking off with street people and handing them little packages and stuff. I don't associate with drug dealers, so I kept my distance. Sorry I can't tell you anything else."

We thank him for the information and move on. Since it's been a long day, we decide to do a pit stop at the bar on the corner of your block. We figure we'll grab a drink and some grub, and maybe someone there will know something about Riley.

As we enter, the dark oak booths are all jammed with patrons devouring beef on French rolls. It's one of several places downtown that's been around for a century and claims to be the originator of the French dip sandwich. There's no one alive to settle the dispute, I guess. There's a nondescript door in the back that leads to a little speakeasy, a remnant from the days of Prohibition. With nowhere else to sit, we hop on stools at the long bar and order a couple of drinks. I'm usually partial to a cold IPA, but after a day like today, it's going to be a single malt Scotch for me.

The bartender, an attractive woman of about forty, brings our drinks and takes our food order. She looks like she knows the lay of the land, so I ask if she remembers seeing a local who looks like you and likes to peep in the neighbors' windows. It takes a minute, but she catches on.

"Oh, right. I've seen this Riley out in front of the bar a few times. Seems like a shady person. My manager says Riley's probably a dealer, always acting suspiciously around the homeless people. I always thought that was pretty dicey dealing to homeless people. I read like 75% of homeless people are mentally ill."

She heads back to place our food orders. We're suddenly startled by an outburst from the guy sitting next to us at the bar, shouting at the television in the corner where a basketball game has just concluded. Middle-aged and balding, he apparently came to the bar alone tonight because he's chosen us to share in his ecstasy. He's a gambler who says he just won a bet on the game right as the last shot went through the net.

"Wow, I had the favorite laying eight points. They hit a shot right at the end to win by nine, so I won by the skin of my teeth. Vegas is unbelievable! The lines they put out are so accurate, I'm always sweating right down to the last second!"

I snap a look to you, as you seem mildly amused by this character. I ask if you've ever gambled on a sporting event or ever known anyone who did. "So, what do you think? Do a lot of these games come right down to the wire against the spread?"

#

You give me your thoughts, and then I turn to the gambler to deliver the surprising news. "Have you ever heard of attentional bias?" The gambler shakes his head. "Well, it's a cognitive bias where you give hyperattention to threatening stimuli and tend to ignore neutral stimuli. In the case of gambling, you tend to take notice when a game comes down to the wire, because you are under a great threat of losing and your emotions are high. For games where you are winning easily against the spread or are getting blown out and don't have any chance of winning, you are more resolved to the outcome and don't experience the same level of threat, so you tend to forget those games.

"In fact, in a recent NFL season, 58% of the outcomes for the entire season were more than 7 points from the Vegas spread. 33% of the outcomes were more than 14 points from the Vegas spread. Only 19% of the outcomes fell within 3 points of the Vegas spread. In other words, a monkey could guess the outcomes of games as well as Vegas oddsmakers."

The gambler seems rather surprised by these numbers. But he quickly turns his attention to the next game and wants to know your opinion. "The next game is about to fire and I need to get a quick bet down. I'm trying to decide between taking the favorite or the underdog. But here's the thing: favorites have won 7 games in a row. Do you think I should jump on the hot streak and take the favorite, or do you think the odds are due to swing back in the favor of the underdog?

#

As you're giving that some thought, the gambler looks down at his smartphone. "Okay, I just got texts from a couple of buddies. My friend Dan says to bet the favorite. Dan's only won about 50% of his bets so far this season, but he's won his last 5 in a row. My friend Steve says to bet the underdog. He's won over 60% of his bets this season, but he's lost his last 4 bets in a row. So, do you go with Dan, who wins a lower percentage of his bets but is on a hot streak? Or do you go with Steve, who wins a higher percentage of his bets but is on a losing streak?"

#

As you're mulling that over, I step in and deliver more surprising news to our gambler friend. "Listen, I'm gonna save you the trouble. You don't have to worry about hot streaks or anything else. Just pull out a coin and flip it, because that'll give you just as much chance of winning as anything else.

"You see, the first mistake you made was committing the gambler's fallacy. The gambler's fallacy is the erroneous belief that if a random event occurs more frequently than normal in the past, it is less likely to happen in the future, or vice versa. Probability has no memory, so it doesn't care that the favorites won 7 in a row against the spread. That doesn't make it more or less likely that the favorite will win the next game.

"And as for Dan and Steve, you committed a hot-hand fallacy. A hot-hand fallacy is the erroneous belief that a person who experiences a successful random outcome has a greater chance of success in further attempts. Again, probability has no memory and the chances of winning a sports bet are always the same as flipping heads or tails. Steve may have correctly picked 60% of his bets so far this season, but over time his winning percentage is going to revert back towards 50%, like every other gambler."

The gambler looks at me like I have two heads and calls another friend for advice. If there's one thing I've learned over the years, gamblers are among the last people in the world to accept the cold hard reality of statistics and probability.

After wolfing down our French dips, we saunter out of the bar and into the night air. It's been a long day and it's about time to wrap up and get a good night's sleep. As we waltz back toward your apartment, we pass in front of a fast-food chicken joint, and a homeless woman approaches us.

"Excuse me. Do you think you could possibly buy me an order of chicken? I'm really hungry."

I turn to you and ask, "How likely would you be to buy her a fast food meal on a scale of 1-10?"

#

"Earlier in the day, I asked you how likely you would be to give a small donation to the homeless charity. Did you give about the same rating for the homeless charity as you did the homeless woman looking for a meal? If you said you'd be more likely to give the homeless woman a meal, then you may have experienced the identifiable victim effect. The identifiable victim effects refers to the tendency to offer greater aid when a specific, identifiable person is observed under hardship, as compared to a large, vaguely defined group with the same need. Many people would be more inclined to give money to a single person in need rather than give a charity the same amount of money, even if the charity serves the exact same type of need."

We arrive back at your apartment. Before we part ways for the night, I ask if it's okay for me to look around for a minute. After all, you're renting a furnished apartment, and it might not be a bad idea to see if Riley might have left any clue behind. It's a long shot, but worth a look. You walk me through your apartment, opening a handful of cupboards and closets. You point out that the closets were mostly empty when you moved in and the cupboards in the kitchen just contained the basics like plates and silverware.

We walk into the living room and I survey the area. I notice there's a cloth draped over the coffee table in the center of the room. I ask what type of coffee table is underneath, and you admit you hadn't ever lifted the covering. So I lean down and pull back the coffee table covering, revealing that the coffee table is actually a trunk with a lid. I turn the latch and lift the lid to the trunk, revealing a handful of items inside the trunk.

I pull out the first item, a bag of brand-new hypodermic needles. Underneath is a stack of photos. Perusing through the photos, we see numerous shots of the apartment building across the street, from the vantage point of your apartment window. Stamped on the photos is a series of dates and times.

I give you a curious look. "This might be dumb question, but what do you think is the meaning of these hypodermic needles?"

\#

"And what about these photos? Can you think of any reason Riley would have taken pictures of people's apartments?"

\#

We place the items back in the trunk. Now we're really intrigued to see what Riley's emergency contact has to say.

Chapter 7

We make our way to the north end of downtown first thing in the morning, brushing past a horde of Chinese immigrants and curious tourists walking along Broadway. The emergency contact on Riley's apartment application works out of a plain gray concrete building in Chinatown right above a Chinese gift shop.

Getting out of the elevator on the fourth and final floor, we make our way to a small office suite in the corner of the building. We enter but don't see a receptionist behind the desk. We don't see anyone at all, just several sparsely decorated offices overlooking the Chinese shopping district below. So I call out to see if anyone is around. After a moment, a worn-looking woman peeks out of a back office and looks at us curiously. I explain whom we're here to see, and she confirms we found the right person.

She invites us back into her office and apologizes for the mess. As we sit, I mention how quiet the office is. She explains that it's a homeless charity and most of the employees are out in the field throughout the day. She says she is the director of the charity and complains how exhausting the work is.

"Homelessness is such a massive problem here. Los Angeles has the largest homeless population in the country. And what makes it even tougher, a lot of homeless people suffer from mental illness. Do you have any idea what percentage of homeless people are mentally ill?"

#

She can't avoid shaking her head just thinking about it. "It's about 20 to 25%." I turn to see your reaction. "Is that close to what you guessed? Many people would have guessed around 75 or 80%. That could be because of their own stereotypes of homeless people, which as we discussed is a type of attribute substitution. It could be because of attentional bias, since people tend to take more notice of raving homeless people and ignore most who keep to themselves. Or it could be because of a cognitive bias known as illusory truth effect. Illusory truth effect is the tendency to believe false information to be correct after repeated exposure.

"Did you remember that the apartment manager claimed 80% of homeless people are mentally ill, and the bartender claimed it was 75%? If you guessed a percentage somewhere in this range, you may have been influenced by others repeating this false claim. Illusory truth effect is commonly exploited by politicians who repeat the same false claim over and over, knowing that people will be more inclined to believe something is true if they are exposed to it often enough."

While we're on the subject, I mention to the charity director something the apartment manager said to us at the time he was talking about homeless people being mentally ill. He said that being on the streets is so stressful that it drives homeless people to mental illness. The charity owner chuckles.

"I think your apartment manager has that backwards. Yes, living on the streets is extremely trying, and it exacerbates existing psychological problems. But mental illness itself is what leads to homelessness, not that other way around. Mentally ill people have a tough time keeping jobs and maintaining healthy connections to friends and family, so many of them end up isolated and incapable of keeping a roof over their heads."

I turn to you and elaborate. "Did you happen to catch that fallacy when the apartment manager stated it? It's called the swimmer's body illusion. The swimmer's body illusion occurs when we confuse selection factors with results. People think they can get a swimmer's body just by training hard. However, professional swimmers don't have their kind of body because they train hard; rather, they are good swimmers because they have that kind of body.

"Don't misunderstand, champion swimmers do train very hard, and you can certainly improve your physique and become a better swimmer by training hard. Yet champion swimmers all have some combination of exceptional lung capacity, a long trunk and short legs, and tremendous natural flexibility. In other words, they have natural selection factors that make them suited to become champion swimmers.

"Think of it another way. The average height of an NBA player is six feet, seven inches. They didn't get tall by training hard. Just as most mentally ill homeless people didn't get mentally ill by being homeless."

I turn to the charity director and express sympathy for the difficulty of her job. I tell her that your neighbor mentioned something about a new program they started last year in Westport and asked if that has been successful.

"Oh, absolutely. So far, they've gotten 67% of homeless people jobs and housing, and now they're no longer on the streets."

I turn to you and remind you that your neighbor in the hallway told us about the zero-tolerance policy in Westport where homeless encampments are outlawed, and homeless people are being arrested for violating this law.

"Now that you know 67% of homeless people in Westport have gotten jobs and housing, how would you rate the new law on a scale of 1-10?"

#

The charity director interjects. "Oh, wait. You're talking about the zero-tolerance policy in Westport. Sorry, I got confused and thought you were talking about another city down south where businesses hire homeless people and give them on-the-job training. That's led to a 67% reduction in homelessness. No, the Westport law has been a disaster. It's had no effect on reducing homelessness and has caused massive overcrowding in Westport's jail system."

I turn back to you. "Okay, let's try this again. Now that you've gotten clarification on the results of the new Westport law, how would you rate the new law on a scale of 1-10?"

#

"You've now rated the Westport law three times: one before you knew the outcome, one after you were told the outcome was positive, and one after you were told the outcome was negative. Did your rating of the law go up when you heard the positive outcome? Did it go down when you heard the negative outcome? If so, you were influenced by outcome bias. Outcome bias is when you evaluate the quality of a decision after the outcome of that decision is already known. Outcome bias is evident when the same behavior produces more ethical condemnation when it happens to produce a bad outcome rather than a good outcome.

"This is not to say that outcomes aren't relevant in evaluating behavior. Naturally, life is full of tough decisions. Sometimes we are surprised when choices we disagree with end up producing positive results. And sometimes perfectly good intentions result in negative unintended consequences. So it is important to consider outcomes when pondering future decisions. But outcome bias causes us to focus too narrowly on aspects of the outcome while ignoring other moral or ethical consequences that are often known when the decision was made.

"In the Westport case, regardless of whether the new law ultimately reduced homelessness, there were serious ethical and Constitutional issues with imprisoning people for being homeless and living on the streets. These issues don't go away merely because you learn that the law reduced homelessness. There are nations in the world that execute people for committing some infractions that we consider misdemeanors. Despite the fact that such draconian laws do result in fewer infractions, most of us value the higher principle of human rights over the narrowly defined positive outcome of reduced infractions.

"Outcome bias often involves outcomes that are random. For example, it's been observed that fans of European football will rate a player's performance higher if he played poorly but scored a lucky goal near the end, and they will rate another player's performance lower if he played a great match but failed to score a goal."

We move on to our reason for being here. I explain to the charity director about the shootings and how we're concerned Riley may have been targeted. I ask if she knows where we can find Riley.

"Well, I knew Riley but unfortunately haven't been in contact in a couple of months. Riley did some work for our charity, distributing food and clothing to the homeless, and even passing out hypodermic needless to heroin users. You know, it's not ideal, but we pass out new hypodermic needles because it cuts down the spread of disease."

She tells us she doesn't know where Riley is now and doesn't have any more information. She does recall a picture that was taken of all the staff at a holiday party, so she searches through several drawers until locating it. Lucky for us, Riley is in the picture. And sure enough, Riley does look remarkably like you. She gives us the picture to help on our search, and we thank her before making our way back to the busy streets of Chinatown.

Walking down the sidewalk, we notice a cluster of homeless people on our side of the sidewalk. I turn to you and smile. "If our gambler friend from last night were betting on whether they ask us for money, what percentage chance do you think a homeless person on the sidewalk will ask you for money as you pass by?"

#

"Most people will guess a pretty high percentage. But studies show that only a small percentage of homeless people panhandle. And those who do panhandle are not doing it all day to everyone they meet. The reason people would guess a high number is because they tend to notice when homeless people ask them for money because it's unpleasant or threatening, and they don't notice when homeless people don't ask them for money, because it's uneventful. As you might recall, this is what we call attentional bias."

We continue to make our way back towards your neighborhood, reflecting on our meeting with the charity director. "Let me ask you, what were your initial thoughts when people in the neighborhood told us that Riley was hanging out with homeless people? Did you think Riley may have been dealing drugs? If so, you may have been influenced by the bandwagon effect. The bandwagon effect is a cognitive bias where you tend to accept beliefs, ideas, fads and trends the more they have already been adopted by others. In other words, we have the tendency to jump on the bandwagon.

"As you probably recall, several people we interviewed expressed the opinion that Riley was dealing drugs to the homeless. Yet no one provided any evidence. If no one had expressed this opinion, you may not have been inclined to think of drug dealing at all. If one person had expressed this opinion but several others expressed a totally different opinion, you may have leaned towards the majority opinion because of the bandwagon effect.

"And there's another reason you might have believed Riley was either a drug dealer or drug user: our discovery of the hypodermic needles in the trunk. If you interpreted the presence of hypodermic needs as evidence of drug dealing, you may have been influenced by belief bias. Belief bias is the tendency to judge the strength of arguments based on the plausibility of their conclusion rather than how strongly the arguments support that conclusion. A person is more likely to accept an argument that supports a conclusion that aligns with existing values, beliefs and prior knowledge, while rejecting counterarguments to the conclusion.

"In this case, if you already had the belief that Riley was a drug dealer, belief bias would cause you to interpret the hypodermic needles as proof of drug dealing. This conclusion seems logical based upon the established belief, but there are other plausible explanations as to why someone would own hypodermic needles, such as being a medical practitioner or a diabetic."

With the suspicion of Riley being a drug dealer off the table, we decide to look a little harder at the stalker angle, and whether Riley might have made an enemy peeping into apartments around the neighborhood. So we head back to your apartment and study the photographs we found in the chest last night.

The stack of photographs all shows the same apartment building across the street from the vantage point of your apartment window. The angle is fairly wide, so we can see several floors in each of the photos. The only detectable difference among the photos is that they all have different time and date stamps.

After a minute of studying the photos, we decipher that there are two sets of photos each day, one early in the evening and one later at night, but all taken around the same times day after day. Then something catches my eye. I lay out all the photos on your sofa in two rows. The first row shows all the early evening photos from each consecutive day. The second row shows all the late night photos from each consecutive day. Suddenly, a clear pattern emerges. I motion you towards the middle of the early evening photos.

"Look at all these floors in the middle of the building. In the early evening, the same apartments are illuminated day after day at the same time, while the dark apartments remain consistent day after day, also at the same time. Now take a look at all the photos from later at night. A number of the apartments that were illuminated are now dark, while many of the dark apartments are now illuminated. But again, it shows the exact same pattern day after day. In other words, there are two different schemes of illuminated apartments, one in the early evening and one later at night. But those same schemes repeat exactly the same way night after night."

We look at each other mystified. "There seems to be some sort of code in the light pattern. But the question is, what does the code mean… and who is it intended for?"

Chapter 8

With the discovery of the pattern in the photographs, we can't avoid the temptation to stare out your side window at the apartment building opposite yours, trying desperately to find a clue that would tip us off as to the meaning of the light code. But it's still early in the day, so the sun's glare off the apartment windows obscures our ability to see inside.

After a minute or so, my eyes drift from building to building and ultimately halt on a parking lot at the end of the next block. It's a rather large parking lot that takes up half a city block, one of the few lots around downtown that haven't been sold off to a developer. What catches my eye in particular are the series of light poles scattered around the lot. Mounted atop each of them are what appear to be security cameras.

I suggest we investigate and see if by some chance we can get access to some of the security footage. The lot is too far away from your building, so the cameras wouldn't have captured the shootings, but perhaps they would contain some evidence of Riley's comings and goings. It's another long shot, but worth a try.

When we arrive at the parking lot, the attendant directs us to a small building in the back corner of the lot which he says is the manager's office. We walk back to the small, single-floor shack and knock on the door. A man in his mid-thirties dressed in slacks and a collared shirt opens the door and gives us a curious look. I explain to him why we're there and inquire as to whether it would even be possible to review security tape from a couple of weeks ago around the time Riley moved out of your apartment. The manager gives us the disappointing news: all security footage is wiped after a week. Even if there was a needle in this haystack, the haystack has already gone up in flames.

We thank him for his time and turn to leave, but he calls out for us to wait a minute. "Listen, from what you told me, I'm not even sure two-week-old footage would have helped you anyway. You need to figure out where this Riley is now.

And I think I may be able to help. My company owns properties all around downtown, and we have security cameras at every location. Half the people downtown walk in front of one of our security cameras every day.

"But here's the thing. All our security footage goes into a cloud server. If we ever record someone committing a crime on one of our cameras, such as breaking into a car, we can run their face through facial recognition software and compare them against a huge database of mugshots to match the face to an identity, assuming they've been arrested before. In addition, the software has an alert system, so it will send us an email notification right when an offender passes in front of one of our properties.

"Here's my thinking. If you give me a picture of your friend Riley, I can set up the system to notify you anytime Riley walks in front of any of our cameras. And if Riley is still living or working downtown, I guarantee we'll find a match. I'm not really supposed to do this for people outside the company, but I could probably make this happen if you're willing to pay a fee."

Our interest is definitely piqued, so we inquire as to exactly how much this is going to cost you. The manager thinks for a moment, and then lays out some options.

"Listen, this is extremely expensive technology, so it's going to cost a bit. But I'll give you three options and let you choose which arrangement works best for you. Option one is you can pay $350 per week. Option two is you can pay $1000 per month. And option three is you can pay $2500 for two months. So it's $350 per week, $1000 per month, or $2500 for two months. Which would you prefer?"

#

I smile because I realize this isn't the first time the manager has negotiated a deal. "He just used what's called the decoy effect. The decoy effect is when consumers tend to have a specific change in preference between two options when a third option is presented that is inferior in all respects to one of the options.

"In this case, the third option of $2500 is a better deal than the first option of $350 per week, when calculated on a weekly basis. But it is worse in price and time commitment compared to the second option of $1000 per month. The third option is essentially a throw-away option intended to push you towards the second option of $1000 per month and away from the first option of $350 per week. Marketers always want to get as much money in the door as possible, so they'd rather you pay $1000 now, even though it averages out to less money per week than option one.

"The best way to avoid being influenced by the decoy effect is to psychologically remove the decoy from consideration. Then return to the other legitimate options and make a choice based on how long you think you'll need the service and how well you think the service will work."

You're obviously interested in this service if it can help us locate Riley. But you want to make sure it's going to work, so you ask the manager how accurate this system is at identifying faces.

"Oh, it's tremendously accurate. This system is rated at 99% accuracy with only a 1% false positive rate. In other words, only 1% of the people it captures will be misidentified as a match."

Since you're going to be paying for the service, I want to make sure you're satisfied with the accuracy of the system.

"So just to make sure you are totally clear about this, whenever you get an alert of a match, how accurate do you expect that match will be?"

#

"If you thought it would be 99% accurate, you fell for the trap of base rate fallacy, and you're setting yourself up for days of tedious frustration. Base rate fallacy is the tendency to give more weight to event-specific information and ignore base rates entirely. One type of base rate fallacy is the false positive paradox, where false positive tests are more probable than true positive tests, occurring when the overall population has a low incidence of a condition and the incidence rate is lower than the false positive rate.

"And that's exactly what we have here. The manager claims the system is 99% accurate, meaning the system will only make a false match 1% of the time. That sounds great. The problem is, his cameras are placed all around downtown and might capture literally hundreds of thousands of people over the course of a week. Only one of them can be Riley. With a 1% false positive rate, this means you will get thousands of match notifications every week that are totally erroneous as you wait for one single correct match of Riley. So when I asked you, whenever you get an alert of a match, how accurate do you expect that match will be? The correct answer is, a small fraction of 1%."

After further consideration, we both agree that we can make more valuable use of our time than spending countless hours per week sifting through bogus matches. We thank the manager for his offer and head back towards your apartment. On the way there, I'm curious about something and try to jog your memory.

"Can you remember the first time you and I discussed anything about a bar? Where were we in our investigation when one of us first mentioned a bar?"

#

"If you thought the first time we discussed a bar was when we had dinner and spoke with the bartender and the gambler, you may have been influenced by observational selection bias. Observational selection bias is the tendency to notice something more when something causes us to be more aware of it. It's not new or suddenly more common; you're just suddenly noticing it.

"In the case of the bar, you and I actually discussed the bar in our first conversation in my office. I also mentioned a bar when I told you the next morning about the philanderer who met his mistress at a wine bar. But those instances are forgettable because you weren't directly associated with the bar. When we finally entered a bar and interacted with people at the bar, it made the bar more significant in your mind. This is the same phenomenon that causes people to believe they are suddenly seeing a model of car much more frequently, when in fact they're only noticing it more often because they just purchased the same model."

After grabbing a quick bite, we arrive back at your apartment just as the sun is setting behind the nearby skyscrapers. Looking out your apartment windows, we now have better visibility into the apartments across the street. You offer me an IPA and we nestle into what could be a long, boring night staring at a building. Not long after we sit down, we start to observe a number of apartments illuminate in random succession across several floors. After about ten minutes, the light pattern on those floors now matches the early evening photos spread out on your sofa.

We scour those apartments to detect any activity that would explain the meaning of the code. Strangely, despite the lights in those apartments suddenly illuminating, we are not able to see a single person occupying those apartments who could account for turning on the lights.

I take a slow sip of beer and look over in your direction. "So now, we've got dozens of furnished apartments where the lights turn magically on and off, but no sign of anyone living there. Who or what is turning those lights on and off? And why?"

Chapter 9

The following morning, I do some research on the apartment building across from you. I discover it's owned by a developer who's built quite a number of new developments around the city, many in the downtown area. The developer specializes in high-end apartments and condos like the one across from you. I find numerous articles featuring the developer commenting on real estate in Los Angeles, mostly repeating the LA real estate mantra that we desperately need to build more housing to keep up with demand.

It's true that Los Angeles fell behind in developing enough housing to meet its growing population. The city, like the rest of the country, experienced three massive real estate crashes in the span of fifteen years, which hurt progress. Plus, a lot of residents opposed new housing construction because of the city already being congested with automobiles and suffering from insufficient public transportation. The real estate cheerleaders lauded new development as the silver bullet to solve the homeless crisis, ignoring the glaring irony that, as new developments increased, so did the homeless population.

So I don't find it particularly strange that this developer has been advocating for new developments. But what I do find a little weird is why a real estate developer is using his expensive new developments to generate massive lighting cues. And I also find it a bit odd that he's been able to secure so many approvals for new developments, because it's not easy getting past city council. I notice in a number of articles that the developer seems to be pretty tight with one particular Los Angeles councilwoman, so you and I decide to make a trip over to City Hall and see if we can get a word with her.

We enter the stone arches under the iconic white tower of LA City Hall off Spring Street, a sight familiar to any fans of LA noir films. We get lucky and catch the councilwoman leaving a meeting and on the verge of heading back to her Silverlake office. She initially tries to give us the brush off, but on hearing the name Jack Wilshire, she opts to lend us her ear for a couple of minutes. I'd like to say it was my distinguished eighteen years on the force that got her attention, or the fact that the bullet I took got me on the front page of the LA Times. But no doubt the real reason she stopped when she heard my name was because one of my previous clients was the wife of the former mayor. Let's just say it didn't end well for the mayor, and word gets around City Hall. The councilwoman apologizes for being curt.

"Sorry, we just came out of a heated meeting. We're trying to decide between two spending proposals. One is a security initiative that would virtually eliminate violent crimes committed by homeless people downtown. The other is a highway safety measure that would reduce highway traffic accidents by 20%. Since everyone seems to have an opinion, would you like to put your two cents in on which proposal you would choose?"

#

While you're mulling over your choice, the councilwoman tells us that most of the people in the meeting preferred to spend the money eliminating violent crimes committed by the homeless. I interject, "Yeah, that's not surprising. A lot of people are influenced by zero-risk bias. Zero-risk bias is preferring to reduce a small risk to zero instead of choosing a greater reduction in a larger risk. Despite the stereotypes about homeless people, the number of violent crimes committed by homeless people in Downtown Los Angeles pales in comparison to the number of accidents on LA freeways. A 20% reduction in car accidents would benefit far more people than eliminating attacks by the homeless.

"Zero-risk bias is what drives taxpayers to advocate spending billions on eliminating a very low risk, such as terrorism, rather than investing the same money reducing a much higher risk, like people getting sick and not being able to afford medical treatment."

The councilwoman hardly seems moved by the discussion, so I get to the matter at hand. I explain that we're investigating a complicated case and are trying to learn more about the process of getting approval for massive real estate developments. She spouts off a list of things like zoning regulations, environmental reviews and building permits. But then she says something that catches our ears.

"And if you're talking about large multi-family residential housing, like apartment buildings and condos, developers get preferential treatment if their existing properties maintain an occupancy rate above 90%. That's a new law that was passed a few years ago, and all landlords and developers need to certify their occupancy rates with the Department of Housing."

The councilwoman apologizes for being out of time and excuses herself from the conversation. That's fine with us, because we have a date with the Los Angeles Department of Housing. I have my suspicions about the occupancy rates of a developer who uses several floors of his apartment building as a light show.

We head down to a modern, nine-story building on Seventh Street on the outskirts of downtown, just to the other side of the 110 Freeway. After being redirected to three different offices, we finally find a clerk who knows anything about landlord occupancy rates. He says they are filed with his office and signed off by a housing inspector. But when we ask about pulling the paperwork filed by the developer of the apartment building across from you, he tells us the bad news that you need to submit a formal request for those records which can take 30 days to process.

We do our best to convince him of the dire circumstances, but getting compassion from a government employee is like getting steak out of a dog's mouth. So I play the only card we have, a card that features a president's face in place of a king or queen. That gets his attention.

"Well, I could get fired if I get caught doing this. So you better make this worth my while. How much are you willing to pay me to get you those occupancy rates?"

#

After you mull over how much cash you're willing to spring for, the clerk throws a number at us. "How about you pay me $500?" You give that some thought.

#

We tell the clerk it's way too much money, and we ask him to be more reasonable. "Okay, fine. But you still need to give me something that makes it worth the risk. I'll take $150 and no less. Do you want to do this or not?"

#

I turn to you and ask, "How does that amount compare to what you originally wanted to pay? If it was higher than you originally wanted to pay, but you were more willing to pay it when the clerk came down from $500, then you were influenced by anchoring bias. Hopefully, though, you learned your lesson from earlier when the apartment manager tried to anchor you to a higher number."

We proceed to bargain the clerk down a little more, and you covertly hand over the cash. We wait a few minutes while the clerk hunts around for the developer's paperwork. He returns with a stack of occupancy certifications from about a dozen different properties. As we peruse page after page, we see that all the developer's properties are certified by the same housing inspector as having occupancy rates above 90%, including the building across from you.

I turn to you and wonder aloud, "How does a building with several empty floors have an occupancy rate above 90%? Of course, I think we now know the answer to that. And I wonder what the housing inspector is going to say when she finds out she's been duped."

Chapter 10

As we arrive at the inspector's office three floors above, we discover she's about to leave her cramped, cluttered office to head out for inspections. At this point, we don't have any hard evidence that the developer had anything to do with the shootings, nor do we even know for sure if this giant rabbit hole we jumped down has anything to do with the case at all. But we do have evidence of real estate fraud, so we do our civic duty and relate our findings to the inspector, albeit without mentioning the shootings.

We tell the inspector about the apartment illumination pattern and how it appears the developer has furnished several empty floors with lights on automated timers. We tell her we suspect the developer is faking high occupancy rates by staging occupied apartments, both to dupe the inspector as well as anyone else who would see otherwise darkened floors.

We suspect his motive is to beat the competition in getting approval for new development projects.

The inspector's response isn't quite what we expected. She doesn't seem to react much when we give her the goods. She just seems to glare at us, like none of this is a surprise. She doesn't bother to ask about any of the details we discovered in our investigation, but instead drills us about our motive for investigating in the first place.

We don't reveal the real reason we began investigating the developer since we don't want to discuss potential suspects in an attempted murder before we have hard evidence. So instead, we tell her you're producing a documentary on the housing crisis and began observing the light pattern in the building across the street from your apartment. That doesn't seem to satisfy her, as she gives you a suspicious look.

"You say you live across the street from the building on Fifth Street?" You confirm you do. "Then you're working with Riley?"

That hits us like a ton of bricks. Apparently, we've followed more closely in Riley's footsteps than we realized. I stammer and claim we do know Riley and we've previously discussed the matter. She tells us that Riley has already been to her office and made the same allegations. She proffers a weak promise that she'll look into the matter, and then she brushes past us and hustles out the door.

You and I look at each other, aware that we have some decisions to make about the investigation. But first, I want to go over a few things with you. "When you found the photos inside your coffee table chest, I asked you why you think Riley's been taking pictures of apartment windows. If you answered that Riley might be stalking someone or was some kind of voyeur, you might have been influenced by the bandwagon effect. Again, just like the drug dealer claims, many of the people we interviewed implied that Riley was creepily stalking someone.

"And think about our investigation of Riley in general and the various pieces of evidence we gathered over time. First, we discovered the hypodermic needles, then the photos of the apartment building, and ultimately the strange light pattern in the building. As you slowly uncovered the facts about this evidence, how did your suspicions evolve? Did each new piece of evidence cause you to radically change your theory of what happened, or did you only make slight alterations of your original theory based upon new information? Did you maintain suspicions of Riley even as new evidence came to light?

"If so, then you may have succumbed to conservatism bias. Conservatism bias is the tendency to insufficiently revise one's belief when presented with new evidence. In other words, new evidence may cause you to revise your beliefs, but the revision is more conservative than it should be given the weight of the new evidence.

"You probably notice that a lot of cognitive biases connect together. Conservatism bias can happen because of anchoring, and it has a similar effect of confirmation bias and the Semmelweis reflex, where you gravitate to evidence that confirms your theory while ignoring evidence that disconfirms your theory. Regardless of what name it's given or the subtle differences among terms, it's important to realize that all of us have a strong emotional attachment to our perspectives, and we should be willing to continually challenge our own beliefs in order to find truth."

We stop at a Mexican restaurant a block from the Housing Department to refuel and discuss our options before heading back. We both agree that it's probably time to take what we have to the police. We may not be any closer to knowing who tried to kill you. But we now have evidence that the developer committed major criminal fraud, that Riley exposed the fraud, and someone who looks a lot like Riley was targeted twice by a sniper near the developer's property.

The police station handling your case is only about two blocks from your apartment. Getting back to your neighborhood after sundown, we take a shortcut through an alley behind your apartment and past the developer's building. As we shuffle through the quiet alley, we hear a third set of footsteps behind us. But turning around we see nothing except the slight movement of a shadow timed with the sudden halt to the footsteps. Assuming it's just one of the homeless residents searching through a recycle bin, we proceed forward. Again, the third set of footsteps. We turn around and, again, see nothing. But after a moment, a bang like a firecracker echoes through the alley, and a bullet whizzes right past your ear.

We duck behind a dumpster just as another shot rings out. Suddenly the set of footsteps becomes faster and louder as the stalker races towards us. We wedge ourselves between the dumpster and a building and discover a back door to what appears to be a garage. We frantically turn the knob and push the door, but it's locked. Just as the shadow of the stalker lengthens and edges its way towards our feet, the back door suddenly swings open, revealing a distinguished-looking man in his forties looking inquisitively back at us.

With no time to explain, we push past him and slam the door shut. He sees our desperation and has no doubt heard the gunshots, so he motions toward the corner of the garage and calls for us to follow him. We obey his orders and ramble towards a small office, barricading ourselves inside as he shuts the door.

The dank office has one desk at the front with a single leather sofa facing it on the opposite wall. One desk lamp faintly illuminates the room. I reach for my smartphone to call the police, but the signal in the garage is dead. For what seems like an eternity, we wait in silence trying to detect any hint that the stalker tracked us to our hiding spot. Suddenly, there's a soft, slow knock at the door.

Much to our shock, the man who rescued us reaches to unlock the doorknob. Despite our panicked protest, he turns the knob and opens the door. In steps a swarthy fellow dressed in black from head to toe, holding a pistol at his side. The other man turns to us and gives you a particularly curious look. "You're not Riley."

It doesn't take us long to realize we've been chased into the hands of the developer. From a mere three words, we now know the developer is behind the shootings, that he did mistake you for Riley, and that Riley must still be alive. The developer pulls out handful of braided nylon rope and a wide-blade box cutter from the desk drawer. While the developer's hitman holds the gun on us, the developer ties our hands behind our backs and shoves us onto the leather sofa. He turns back to the hitman.

"Go get three guns. One for me and two for the others. We've got some logistics to figure out." The hitman hands the developer his gun and then exits the room.

The developer demands that we tell him where Riley is. We explain we never met Riley and had been trying to track him down because we suspected he was the intended target of the shootings. The developer smirks through his teeth. "I'll tell you what, how about I give you a little break since you've obviously had such rotten luck lately? I'll take all the bullets out of this gun except for one, and we'll play rounds of Russian roulette. If you survive, I'll let you walk. What do you say?"

I give you a skeptical look. "Even if we were to believe the developer is a man of his word, which is highly dubious, what percentage chance would you have to survive this game of Russian roulette?"

#

"Well, the first question you have to ask is, how many bullets does the chamber hold? When you made your calculation, did you assume the gun holds six bullets? Many people would have guessed six because of anchoring bias. TV shows and movies commonly portray handguns as having 6 rounds, so many people get anchored to that number. As it turns out, revolvers typically accommodate between 5 and 10 bullets, depending on caliber, and a semi-automatic pistol carries between 7 and 18 bullets.

"The second question is, does knowing how many bullets fit into the chamber tell you what percentage chance you have of surviving this game of Russian roulette? No, it does not. And if you thought it did, you completely forgot about base rate fallacy. Remember, the developer said you would play rounds of Russian roulette, but he didn't say how many rounds. The number of rounds must be factored into the base rate before you can make a calculation of probability. For example, if there's only one bullet in a chamber that holds ten, and you're only playing one round of the game, then you have a 10% chance of taking a bullet. That might be worth the risk in this situation. But the more rounds you play, the greater your chance of biting the dust."

I turn back to the developer and ask him how many rounds we're playing. He smiles and says, "Fifty." It's a good thing we know about base rate fallacy, because with fifty rounds of the game, your 90% survival rate just went down to about zero. We kindly thank him for his offer, but decline.

A moment later the hitman returns with three guns and sets them in a row on the edge of the desk, spaced evenly apart. He then takes his own gun back from the developer.

The hitman explains to the developer, "One of the guns is loaded, the other two are empty. I need to go upstairs and get more bullets." The hitman exits and the developer nestles into the chair behind the desk with the three guns lined up across from him. The developer picks up an older-model phone sitting on his desk and places a call. We wish we had seen that phone a little earlier. He swivels his chair to the side and begins to talk quietly into the phone.

I look over to see how you're holding up, and I notice that you've managed to get the rope loose from around your wrists, and I can see you eyeing the guns on the desk. I lean over and speak quietly into your ear while the developer is distracted on his call.

"You're not going to have time to grab all three guns. As soon as you jump up, he's going to grab a gun and you might have time to grab one too. The good news is, the hitman didn't tell him which gun is loaded and which ones are empty. So you both have the same chance of picking the loaded gun. Give it a second and think about which gun you are going to grab, the one on the right, the one in the middle, or the one on the left."

#

Suddenly, the hitman pops back into the room and interrupts the developer's phone call. "Sorry, I didn't go up yet. Let me bring one of the empty guns up to Daryl." The hitman reaches over and grabs one of the guns that you didn't choose, leaving only two guns on the desk, but spaced far apart. The hitman exits the room and the developer goes back to his phone conversation.

I look back over to you. "Okay, now you're down to two choices. One gun is loaded and the other is empty. The only question now is, do you want to keep your original choice, or do you want to switch and go for the other gun?"

#

"If you keep your original choice and go for the first gun you selected, you're not only falling victim to cognitive bias, you're doubling your chances of being killed. By keeping your original choice, you have a 33% chance of choosing the loaded gun. If you switch to the other gun, you have a 67% chance of choosing the loaded gun. Before I explain this one to you, just understand that even mathematicians go kicking and screaming debating this problem.

"First, I'll explain the math, then the cognitive biases that lead to the wrong choice. When you started the so-called game, you had three options and only one was correct. You knew at that point you had a 33% chance of being correct. This means that all other options had a 67% chance of being correct. The fact that the hitman came and removed one of the options that he knew was a false option did not affect the probability of the choices; you still had a 33% chance of being correct and all other options still had a 67% chance of being correct. The only thing that changed was that one of the known false options was taken off the table, leaving only one other option.

"Still not convinced? Then imagine there were 100 guns and only one was loaded. If you guessed one of the guns, what chance would you have of being right? One percent. Now, imagine the hitman removed 98 empty guns, leaving just yours and one other gun. Do you think you would suddenly have a 50% chance of having chosen the right gun, despite there having been 99 out of 100 empty guns originally on the table? Of course not; that would be insane. Obviously, the probability would be much different if the hitman didn't know whether he were removing loaded or empty guns, but in this case he knew he was removing false options.

"There are numerous cognitive biases that could cause someone to keep their original choice. First and foremost, they erroneously believe that each of the final two options carries a 50% probability. That erroneous belief is a framing bias, where the person gets trapped into the smaller frame of two options and forgets the larger, more relevant frame of three options.

"And once they accept the frame of two options with 50/50 probability, they would prefer to simply keep their original option because of loss aversion. Loss aversion refers to people's tendency to prefer avoiding losses rather than acquire equivalent gains. In other words, it's better to avoid giving up the loaded gun than to acquire the loaded gun by switching choices. This is due to the fact that once a person owns an item, forgoing it feels like a loss, and humans are loss-averse.

"This problem, sometimes called the Monty Hall Problem after a 1970s game show host, is not something you will commonly encounter in life. But it does remarkably demonstrate how people cling to cognitive bias in order to staunchly guard their belief system. When this problem was presented in a magazine decades ago, thousands of readers, including hundreds with PhDs, wrote to the magazine to refute the idea that switching would increase the odds to 67%. In fact, one of the most prolific mathematicians in history remained unconvinced until he was shown a computer simulation that proved the assertion."

You nod your head and give me a wink. You're going to play the percentages and switch your original choice. You're going for the other gun.

At once, you spring to your feet and lunge towards the desk. You pounce upon one of the guns as the developer drops the phone and grabs the other. You stare at each other in a momentary standoff, as neither one of you knows who has the loaded gun. The developer decides to throw caution to the wind, and... click. He pulls the trigger.

Nothing. You chose the loaded gun. Thank God for simple math. You order the developer to sit in his chair. You untie me and hand me the gun. You grab the rope and tie the developer to his chair. Then we rush out of the office.

Back in the garage, we make a bee line towards the back door. Suddenly, an elevator door opens and out steps the hitman. Spotting us, he withdraws his gun and fires, barely missing us. We dart in and out of cars trying to avoid the hail of bullets coming from the hitman's gun. I'm holding the loaded gun, and I manage to fire back a couple of token shots, but I don't have time to aim so they only serve as a temporary distraction.

We finally make the back door and spring out into the alleyway, a bullet striking the inside of the door just as you pass through. We circle the dumpster and are about to sprint towards the alley exit when suddenly my shoe catches on the bottom corner of the dumpster, launching me face first onto the pavement and sending my gun sliding down the alley floor. You don't realize what's happened until you reach the end of the alley when, upon turning around to check my whereabouts, you see the hitman standing over me with the gun pointed straight at my face.

The hitman glares down the alley at you. "Run away and your friend dies. Come back and I'll let your friend go." Now you another tough choice to make. Do you want to come back or run to the police?

At this moment, you can run to the police and save yourself, but there's a high degree of likelihood that I will die. If you come back, the hitman will let me go, but there's a high degree of likelihood that you will die.

Decisions that involve self-preservation or are made from a place of fear are often subject to zero-sum bias. Zero-sum bias is the belief that one person's gain would be another person's loss, and therefore one's own gain should be prioritized. It's often called fixed-pie thinking. Using the analogy of a pie, if there are eight pieces and three people, zero-sum bias leads you to believe that someone is going to get fewer pieces than the others.

The problem with zero-sum bias is that it's based on a limiting belief system that ignores other non-zero-sum options. For example, you could recut the pie into 9 even pieces. Or you could sell the pie to someone else and use the proceeds to buy groceries that could feed all three of you. Many of the great spiritual leaders throughout history have preached against zero-sum bias and in favor of self-sacrifice and finding universally beneficial solutions to humanity's problems.

This would not be an easy situation to avoid a zero-sum solution. It looks pretty clear cut that one of us is going to die. Or maybe not. Maybe if you run to the police, the hitman will forgo killing me knowing that you would be a living witness to a murder charge. If we do a swap, we will have the same leverage. And maybe you'd prefer to swap positions with me because you feel moral responsibility for having pulled me into this situation in the first place.

The point is, life presents us with surprisingly diverse options if we just open up our minds to see them and stop falling into the trap of thinking from a place of fear. Fortunately for you, however, you don't have to face the consequences of this particular decision. That's because, in the time it takes you to consider your options, someone in the shadows behind the dumpster sneaks around and whacks the hitman over the head with a 2-by-4, dropping him unconscious to the concrete below.

It's the homeless guy. The one you yelled out for ranting and raving outside the bar. As he drops the 2-by-4 to the ground, he swings around in your direction. Cocking his head in confusion, he exclaims, "Wait. You're not Riley!"

Epilogue

We could have never known a sniper's bullet that twice grazed your head would lead to the biggest real estate scandal in Los Angeles history. Billions worth of residential development projects were approved by the city based on fraudulent claims from one of the city's biggest developers. In addition to staging apartments around the city to make them appear occupied, the developer was funneling money to the inspector to make sure the documentation got certified. Now, the developer, hitman and inspector are all sitting in prison awaiting trial for fraud and attempted murder.

Many people questioned the need for such a scheme, considering demand for housing in the city was so elevated. Why not just rent the available units to the surplus of apartment hunters around the Southland? The simple answer is, because most working people can't afford the price of luxury apartments in Los Angeles, so a fair percentage sit empty. And while normal market forces should cause the price of new residential apartments to come down in price when they sit empty for a while, the developer opted for a different financial strategy, one not available to the rest of us.

As zero-percent interest rates spawned a massive California real estate bubble, the developer gobbled up billions in dirt-cheap loans to finance massive real estate construction, which in turn rapidly appreciated in value as the housing market reached nosebleed levels. It wasn't about building housing to serve the needs of a growing population; it was about gaming the system to expand land ownership and inflate asset value. The developer probably figured he'd do what most Twenty-First Century robber barons had done during every other economic bubble, and get out before the whole house of cards came crashing down, leaving some other schmuck holding the bag. Talk about zero-sum bias.

And the developer probably would have gotten away with it, if not for a vigilant homeless advocate who just happened to have a front-row seat to the fraud. Speaking of Riley, we found out from the homeless guy who rescued us that Riley had been in hiding in a Van Nuys studio out in The Valley ever since getting wind of the murder plot. The homeless guy, who typically slept beside the dumpster in the alley, had overheard the developer talking to the hitman about taking out Riley, after learning from the inspector that Riley was onto him. So the homeless guy tipped off Riley, and Riley absconded to Van Nuys. Now you know why the homeless guy was so miffed when Riley, or should I say you, jumped on his case that night before the shootings started.

So, now that the case is solved and you're out of harms way, how well did you do in interpreting each piece of evidence as it was presented, on a scale of 1-10?

#

And how would you rate your level of cognitive bias throughout our investigation on a scale of 1-10?

#

If you remember back to our first night together, I asked you how confident you were in your ability to solve this case. If you overestimated your abilities, you may have been influenced by the Dunning–Kruger effect. The Dunning–Kruger effect is a cognitive bias in which people with low ability at a task overestimate their ability.

You might also remember I asked you at the start to rate your own level of bias on a scale of 1-10, and to also rate the bias of others. How does your answer now compare to your answer at the start? Before going through this kind of process, many people will rate themselves as having relatively low bias, while rating other people as being more biased than themselves. This reveals yet another cognitive bias known as bias blind spot.

Bias blind spot is the ability to recognize the impact of biases on the judgment of others, while failing to see the impact of biases on one's own judgment. You might have noticed that I too operated from cognitive bias. From our very first moments together, I mostly characterized the homeless crisis as having stemmed from urban development and gentrification. While this is certainly a major contributing factor, homelessness is a complex problem caused by myriad factors, from gentrification to economic inequality to mental illness and drug addiction.

Perhaps our adventure opened you up to a more accurate assessment of your own level of cognitive bias, and ideally you became increasingly aware of the traps of cognitive bias as we proceeded through our investigation.

Hopefully you never find yourself in this kind of dire situation again, where succumbing to cognitive bias could have life or death implications. But you are going to make important choices on a daily basis pertaining to relationships, career, politics, commerce and everything else, and you'll want to avoid cognitive biases in order to make more reasoned judgments. So the question is, how can you better identity your own cognitive bias and think more rationally?

Well, the answer is constantly evolving and is the subject of much debate in psychology and neuroscience. It would certainly be helpful to study logic and rhetoric so that you are keener at identifying logical fallacies and deceptive rhetoric that prey on innate cognitive biases.

And it's also an excellent idea to get a basic education of statistics and probability. If you thought statistics and probability was only practical for certain people who work in math and science, then hopefully you now realize that solving many of life's dilemmas require your ability to accurately assess probability. In fact, the neglect of probability is itself a cognitive bias, and influences many other cognitive biases. The neglect of probability is the tendency to disregard probability when making a decision under uncertainty.

For example, when Malaysia Airlines Flight MH370 disappeared over the Indian Ocean years ago, there was no immediate hard evidence of what had happened. In the absence of an explanation, a growing online community surmised the plane must have been seized by aliens. Despite the fact that airline crash statistics are easily searchable and demonstrate a high probability of crashes from mechanical failure and pilot error, and a somewhat lower probability of terrorism and pilot suicide, some people choose to accept an explanation that has an infinitesimal probability. It would be like betting on a football game, except instead of betting the favorite or the underdog, you bet that an asteroid will strike the stadium before the game even finishes.

It's this kind of disconnect from reason that plagues our personal problem-solving and public discourse. Most people are either unaware of their own cognitive biases or unwilling to challenge their existing beliefs and therefore remain targets for manipulation.

Thanks for taking me away from the dull routine for a little while. I wish you the best in your endeavors. If you should ever need my services again, you can always find me in my humble, second-story office on the edge of Little

Tokyo. That is, until they knock down my building for luxury condos and I have to relocate to Van Nuys.

About the Author

Christopher Prince is a Los Angeles-based author, screenwriter and audiobook narrator. In addition to his work on cognitive bias, Christopher has produced dozens of audiobooks ranging from communication patterns, student learning, productive thinking, and Carl Jung. "Cognitive Bias Could Get You Killed" is an educational fiction based upon the discoveries of numerous psychologists and behavioral economists, including Amos Tversky and Daniel Kahneman.

CPSIA information can be obtained
at www.ICGtesting.com
Printed in the USA
FSHW011957280721
83653FS